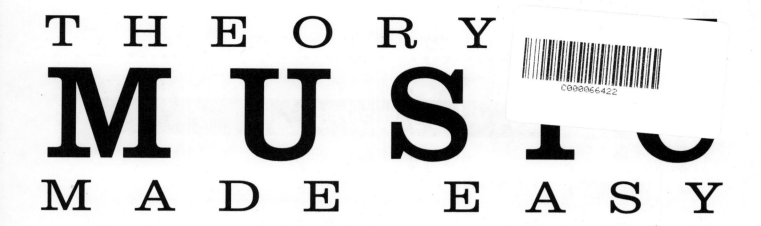

THEORY MUSIC MADE EASY

GRADE 7

Loh Phaik Kheng

© RHYTHM MP SDN. BHD. 1997

Sole Distributor:
RHYTHM MP SDN. BHD.
2060 & 2061, Jalan Persekutuan, Permatang Tinggi Light Industry,
14000 Seberang Perai Tengah,
Penang, Malaysia.
Tel: 04-587 3689 (Direct Line), 04-587 3690 (Hunting Line)
Fax: 04-587 3691
E-mail: rhythm_mp@mphsb.po.my

Published by
RHYTHM MP SDN. BHD.

Cover Design & Pre-press by
CP TECH SDN. BHD.

Printed in Malaysia by
MONOSETIA SDN. BHD.

ISBN 967-985-500-7
Order No.: MPT-3003-07

CONTENTS

Suspension - holding of a note of one chord over to the next chord.

A suspended note must belong to the same voice as the note which it replaced.

A suspended note moves a step down to its note of resolution.

A suspension can occurring in any voice - Soprano, Alto, Tenor, Bass.

Double suspension - occurring at the same time in 2 voices.

Triple suspension - occurring at the same time in 3 voices.

4 kinds of suspensions - 4-3, 6-5, 7-6, 9-8.

(a) 4-3 suspension

(b) 9-8 suspension

(c) 6-5 suspension

(d) 7-6 suspension

Retardation - suspended note resolves up (7-8).

Commonly found in perfect cadence.

1. Rewrite these exercises and add in suspensions where needed.

(N.B. If you think there are more than 1 suspension [double suspension, triple suspension] write them out.)

(N.B. A suspension can sometimes move to adjacent notes or other chord notes before moving to its note of resolution.)

For this question, there is no need to write any figures under root position chords. For chords in other positions i.e. first inversion, second inversion and third inversion, figures are needed to indicate the position of each chord.

Figures for the various positions of the chords	
Root position	$\frac{5}{3}$ or 5 or no figures
First inversion	$\frac{6}{3}$ or 6
Second inversion	$\frac{6}{4}$
For supertonic 7th (II^7) or dominant 7th (V^7) chords	
Root position	$\frac{7}{5}$ or $\frac{7}{5}$ or 7
First inversion	$\frac{6}{5}$
Second inversion	$\frac{6}{4}$ or $\frac{4}{3}$
Third inversion	$\frac{6}{4}$ or $\frac{4}{2}$

The figures for appoggiaturas are the same as the figures for suspensions.

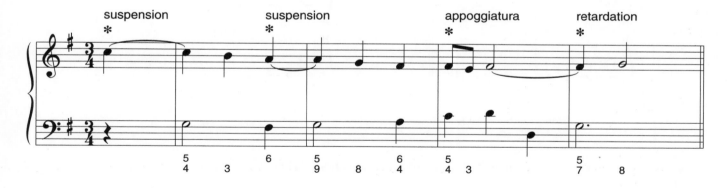

When there is an accidental in the bass, there is no need to write it next to the figure.

But when the accidental is needed for other notes of the chord, it must be written either on the left side or right side of the figure.

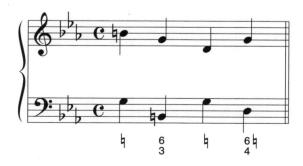

When there is no change in the harmony, a line must drawn under the bass note especially when it is a passing note.

_____   6   _____   6

(N.B. All these figures are actually intervals between the notes of the chords [see Handbook of Music Theory Grade 6 Pages 26 and 27]).

Students are advised to be careful when adding figures to the bass part.
Some intervals can belong to 2 kinds of chords.
To be sure what chord to choose, always look at the next chord.
For example, an interval of a 3rd can belong to a root position chord and also to a first inversion chord.

(a)

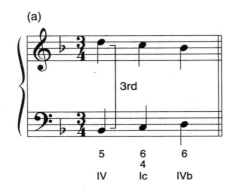

   5   6   6
         4
  IV   Ic IVb

(b)

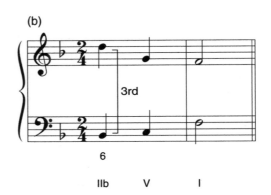

      6
  IIb V   I

In example (a), the interval of a 3rd is taken as a root position chord (IV) because it is part of a passing $\frac{6}{4}$ progression (IV, Ic, IVb).
In example (b), the interval of a 3rd is taken as IIb because the chord that comes after it is chord V followed by chord I (perfect cadence) and IIb is usually used to approach a perfect cadence at the end.

Add figures to the bass part of each of the following.

Look carefully at the other chords before deciding what chord to choose for the interval of a 3rd.

An interval of a 4th belongs to 4 different chords - second inversion ($^6_4$) chord, root position chord with 4-3 suspension, $^4_3$ (V^7c), $^4_2$(V^7d).

(a)

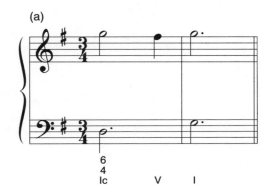

$^6_4$
Ic   V   I

(b)

$^5_4$ 3
IV   I   V

The figure **5** indicates a root position chord.

(c)

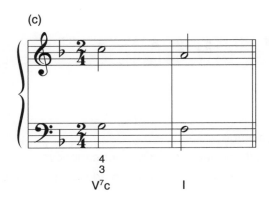

$^4_3$
V^7c I

(d)

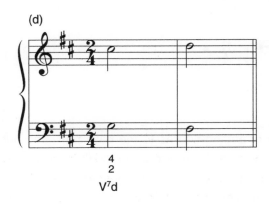

$^4_2$
V^7d

In example (a), the interval of a 4th is taken as a second inversion ($^6_4$) chord because it is part of a cadential $^6_4$.

In example (b), the interval of a 4th is taken as a root position chord with a 4-3 suspension.

In example (c), the interval of a 4th is taken as a V^7c chord resolving to chord I.

In example (d), the interval of a 4th is taken as a V^7d chord resolving to chord Ib.

Add figures to the bass line of each of the following exercises.
Be careful to choose the correct chord for the interval of a 4th.

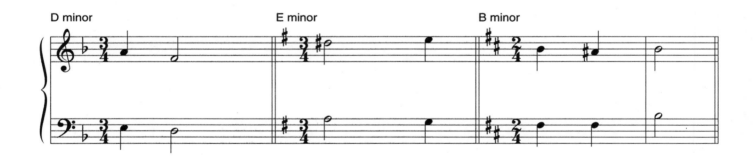

Before adding figures to the bass part, find out the key of the passage.

See whether there are any modulations as these will help to identify perfect and imperfect cadences.

Introduce suspensions in cadences especially in perfect cadence and cadential $\frac{6}{4}$ in order to add harmonic interest and to keep the rhythm going.

Decorate the perfect cadences in both the major and minor keys by a 4-3 suspension in the inner part on the dominant note.

(a)

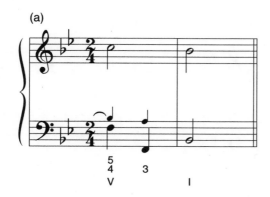

$$\begin{array}{c} 5 \\ 4 \end{array}$$ 3

V   I

(b)

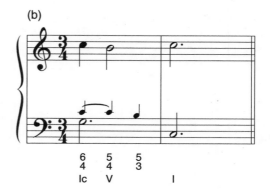

$$\begin{array}{c} 6 \\ 4 \end{array}$$ $$\begin{array}{c} 5 \\ 4 \end{array}$$ $$\begin{array}{c} 5 \\ 3 \end{array}$$

Ic   V   I

In the cadential $\begin{smallmatrix}6\\4\end{smallmatrix}$ in example (b) the dominant chord is delayed by a 4-3 suspension before moving to chord I.

In each of the following exercises, add figures to the bass line and introduce suspensions in the cadence.

If the final cadence is an imperfect cadence, a 7-6 suspension is often shown in the figuring.

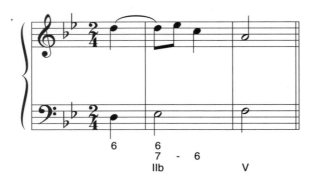

When there is an accidental in the bass part, there is no need to write the accidental below the note. But, when an accidental is needed in the inner part or shown in the top part, the accidental must be written either next to the figure or below the figure (depending on the position of the chord).

C minor:

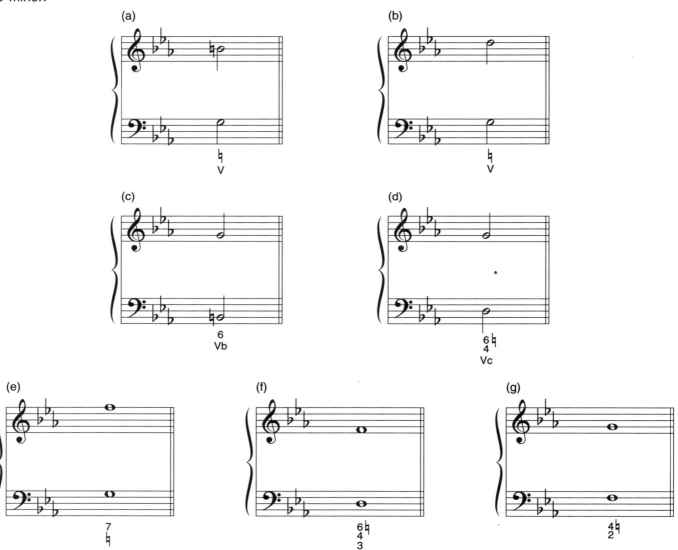

Examples (a) (b) (c) and (d) belong to the dominant chord of C minor.
Examples (e) (f) and (g) belong to the dominant seventh chord of C minor.

Indicate suitable chords for a continuo player by figuring the bass in the following passage. $\frac{5}{3}$ chords need not be shown except where chromatic alteration is required. All other chords should be indicated, as should any suspended dissonances.

Carry on from bar 5

(a)

Carry on from bar 5

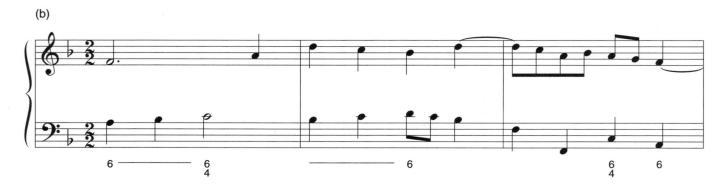

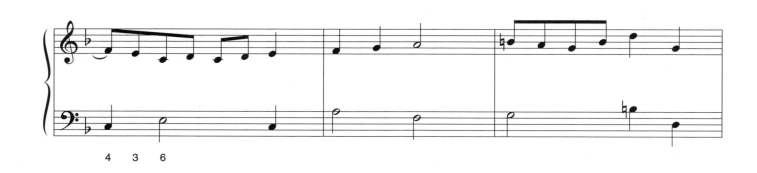

Carry on from bar 4

Carry on from bar 5

(d)

Carry on from bar 3

(e)

Carry on from bar 6

(f)

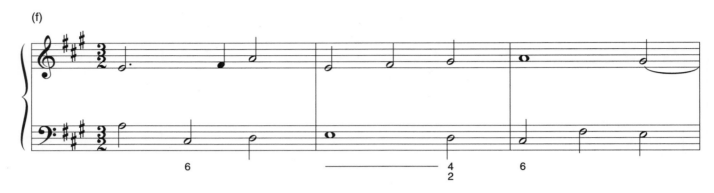

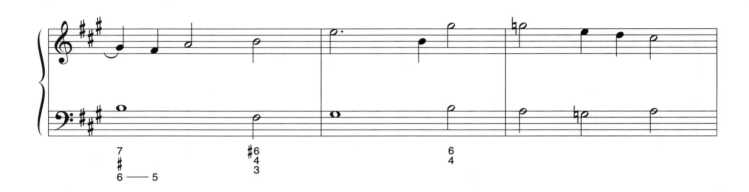

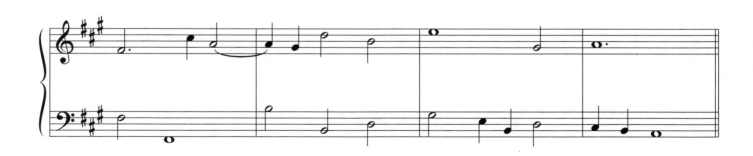

Carry on from bar 5

(g)

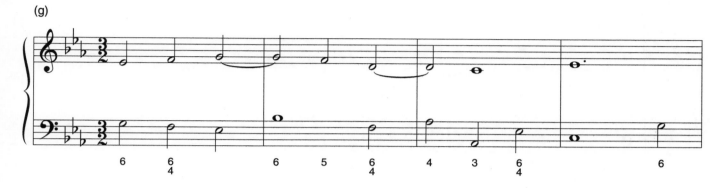

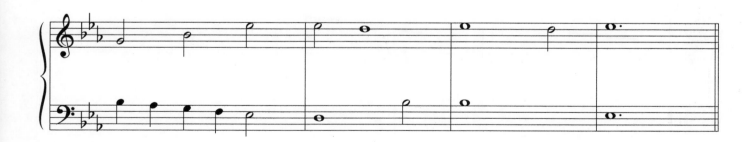

Carry on from bar 5

(h)

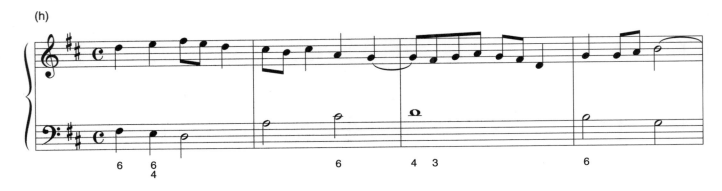

Carry on from bar 6

(i)

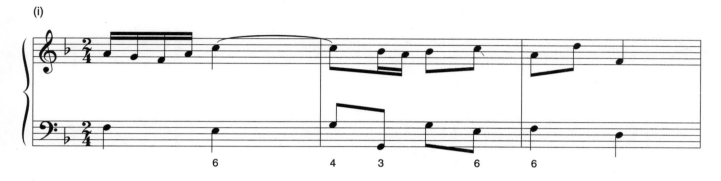

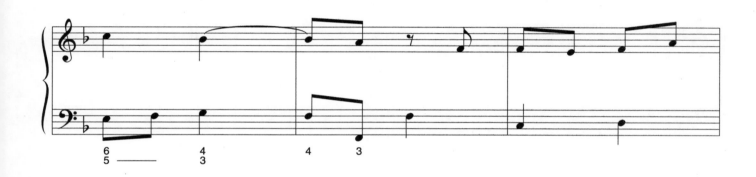

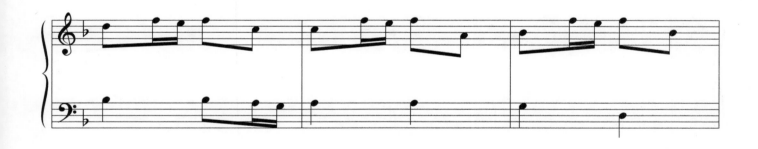

Carry on from bar 6

(j)

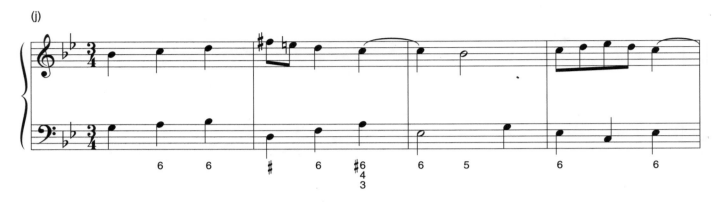

J. S. Bach's chorales are made up of vertical chords and various kinds of melodic decorations - unaccented and accented passing notes, upper and lower auxiliary notes, appoggiaturas and anticipations.
Changing notes are seldom used in J. S. Bach's chorales.
Suspensions and retardations are also found in J. S. Bach's chorales.

• Use of Unaccented Passing Note

The unaccented passing note is more often used in J. S. Bach's chorale because it can bring out the flow in the melodic line.

(N.B. Passing notes can be used at the same time in 2 different voices as long as they do not produce consecutive 5ths and octaves.)

Without Passing notes

With Passing notes

(N.B. To avoid the awkward augmented 2nd between the 6th and 7th notes of the harmonic form, use the melodic form).

Example: C minor

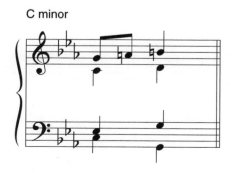

Rewrite the following passages adding unaccented passing notes where needed.

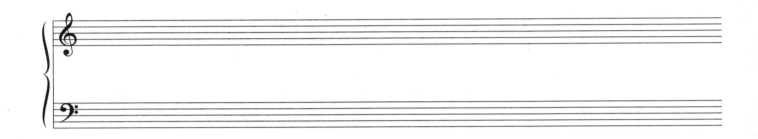

• Use of Accented Passing Notes

The accented passing note is like the unaccented passing note - it comes in between 2 harmony notes which are a 3rd apart. Instead of coming in on the 2nd half of the beat, it comes in on the main beat and is played with the chord on the beat. The harmony note which is replaced by the chord then comes in half a beat later. Accented passing notes can also occur in the bass.

Without accented passing notes

With accented passing notes

accented passing notes

Rewrite the following passages and add in accented passing notes in the alto, tenor and bass.

• Use of the Upper Auxiliary and Lower Auxiliary Notes

In order to produce movement between 2 harmony notes which are the same, auxiliary notes are used.

(N.B. An auxiliary note is like an unaccented passing note - it comes in on the second half of the beat.)

Without auxiliary notes

With auxiliary notes

Rewrite the following passages by adding in auxiliary notes to the alto and tenor parts.

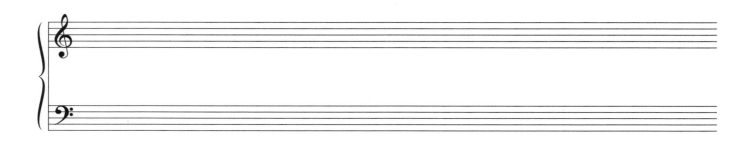

• Use of Appoggiaturas

An appoggiatura is either a step above or a step below the note from which it precedes.

An appoggiatura is just like an accented passing note - it comes on the main beat and is played with the chord.

The harmony note which it replaces then comes in half a beat later.

An appoggiatura may also be approached by a leap unlike the accented passing note.

Without appoggiaturas

With appoggiaturas

Appoggiaturas

Rewrite the following passages by adding in appoggiaturas to the alto and tenor parts.

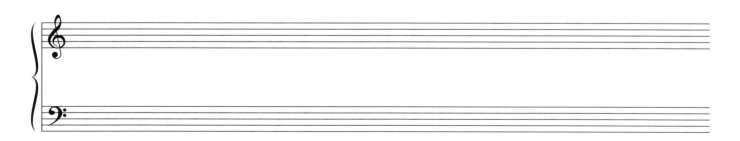

• Use of Suspensions and Retardations

4 - 3, 6 - 5, 7 - 6, 9 - 8 suspensions and retardations (which are common in perfect cadences) are often found in Bach's chorales.

Without suspensions and retardation

With suspensions and retardation

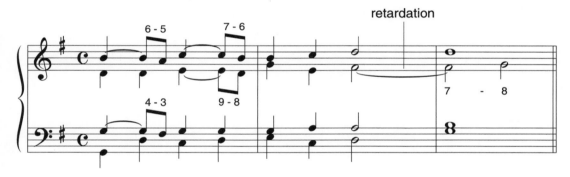

Notes of resolution of suspensions are sometimes decorated but this is more common in instrumental music (fugue, etc.) than in chorale settings for three-part or four-part voices.

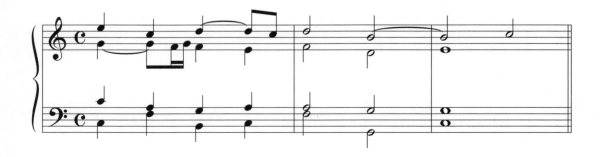

Rewrite the following by adding in suspensions and retardations where needed.

• Use of Subsidiary Harmony Notes

Besides using passing notes and auxiliary notes to produce stepwise movement, an occasional leap of an interval which does not exceed an octave can also be used to add interest to the melody line and the bass line. The note which is used to produce this interval belongs to the chord which is being used.

Without Subsidiary harmony notes

With Subsidiary harmony notes

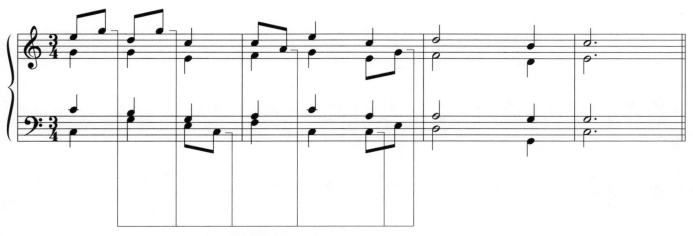

Subsidiary harmony notes

Rewrite the following by adding in subsidiary harmony notes in the bass part.

Rewrite the alto, tenor and bass in the following chorale harmonisation and add some passing and suspended dissonances in the style of J. S. Bach. Begin each exercise as shown.

(a)

(b)

(c)

(d)

(e)

(f)

(g)

(h)

(i)

(j)

The bass of Corelli's trio sonatas and other instrumental works often has a lot of crotchet or quaver movements. Melodic decorations including suspensions are used to decorate the upper 2 parts.

Example:

Rewrite the two violin parts in the following passage to include some passing and suspended dissonances in the style of a trio-sonata by Corelli beginning as shown.

(a)

(b)

(c)

(d)

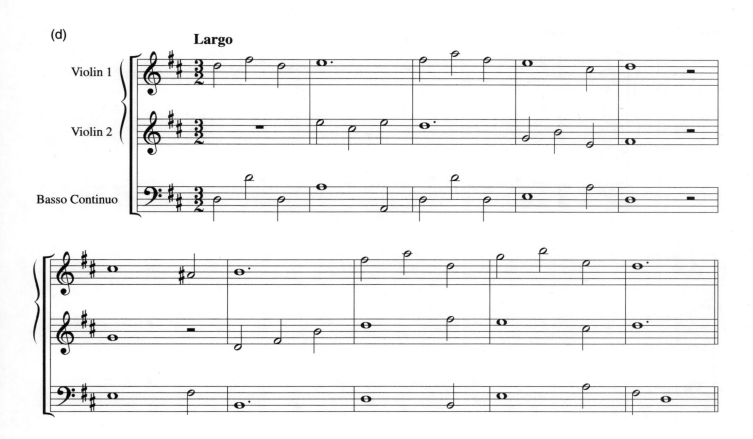

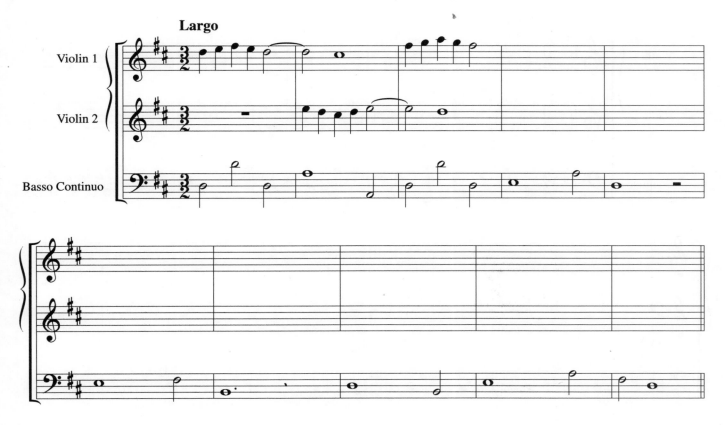

(e)

(f)

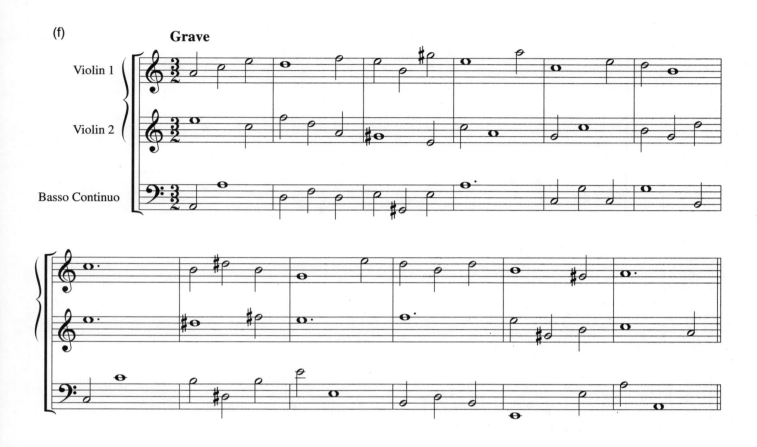

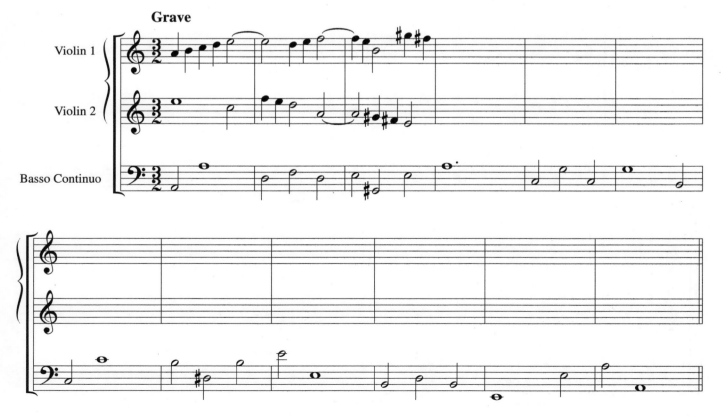

(g)

(h)

(i)

(j)

Things to remember:

1) analyse the chords in the accompaniment,

2) find the cadence points,

3) see whether there are any modulations,

4) see whether the given solo part completes the harmony with the accompaniment,

5) look for imitations, repetitions (near or exact) between the solo part and accompaniment,

6) look for ornaments and non-harmony notes used in the given solo part and accompaniment,

7) try to use the rhythmic pattern of the given opening in your answer.

Things to avoid:

1) merely doubling the solo instrumental line with the harmonic part,

2) writing your melody which is always moving in similar motion with the accompaniment,

3) using notes which are outside the range of the instrument or voice.

Example:

(a) Continue the violin part in the following passage. Add performance directions, including bowing marks to the violin part.

(b) Continue the flute part in the following passage. Add performance directions.

(c) Continue the oboe part in this passage. Add performance directions.

(d) Continue the voice part in the following passage. Add performance directions.

(e) Continue the cello part in the following passage. Add performance directions and bowing marks to the cello part.

(f) Continue the flute part in the following passage. Add performance directions.

(g) Continue the violin part in the following passage. Add performance directions and bowing marks to the violin part.

(h) Continue the cello part in the following passage. Add performance directions and bowing marks to the cello part.

(i) Continue the voice part in the following passage. Add performance directions.

(j)   Continue the oboe part in the following passage.   Add performance directions.

In this section, a short melodic figure (motif) is given and the students are asked to use the figure to compose a melody which is mostly an opening section of a composition which is either an Elegy, a Nocturne, a March, a Fanfare (see Appendix) or any movement.

The given melodic figure can be extended to make a melody of either ten bars or twelve bars by using sequence (tonal or real), imitation, inversion or repetition.
Melodic decorations are also used to elaborate the given figure.

Example:
Compose about ten bars to make an opening movement of a lively dance for unaccompanied flute or violin based on the given melodic figure.
Include performance directions for the instrument of your choice as well as bowing marks for violin.

Instrument: ____Violin____

In the example, the given melodic figure (bars 1 and 2) is repeated a 2nd higher in bars 3 and 4. The first 3 notes of the given figure are repeated 3 times - each time a 2nd higher in bar 5. The notes in bar 2 are inverted in bar 6 and repeated a 2nd lower in bars 7 and 8. The notes in bar 1 are inverted in bar 9.

Sometimes the given melodic figure consists of only a few notes which do not have any rhythm pattern.

Example:

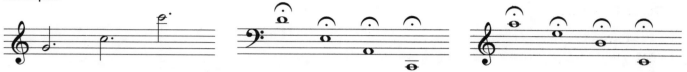

All these figures which are known as *recitando* (free rhythm) figures provide the main pitches on which the melody is based.

The notes of the recitando figures can be used in a different octave from the ones given.

The bars of recitando melodies are not of equal length and this means there are more than one time signature. The time signatures can either be added in or left out.

Example:

Compose about twelve bars to make the opening section of a movement for unaccompanied clarinet or saxophone based on the given figure. Include performance directions for the instrument you choose.

Instrument: Saxophone

In bar 1, the main note F is decorated by other notes to produce a melodic shape which is repeated a 5th higher in bar 2. In bar 3 a new rhythm is formed around the main note D and this is repeated in bar 4 with the main note A written one octave lower. Bars 5 and 6 are written around the main notes G and D. None of the main notes are seen in bar 7 but they appear in bar 8. Bars 9 and 10 have no main notes. The main notes G and D appear again in bar 11. The melody ends with the main note A at its given pitch.

(a) Compose ten bars of an Elegy for tenor trombone or cello based on the given melodic line. Include performance directions for the instruments of your choice as well as bowing marks for cello.

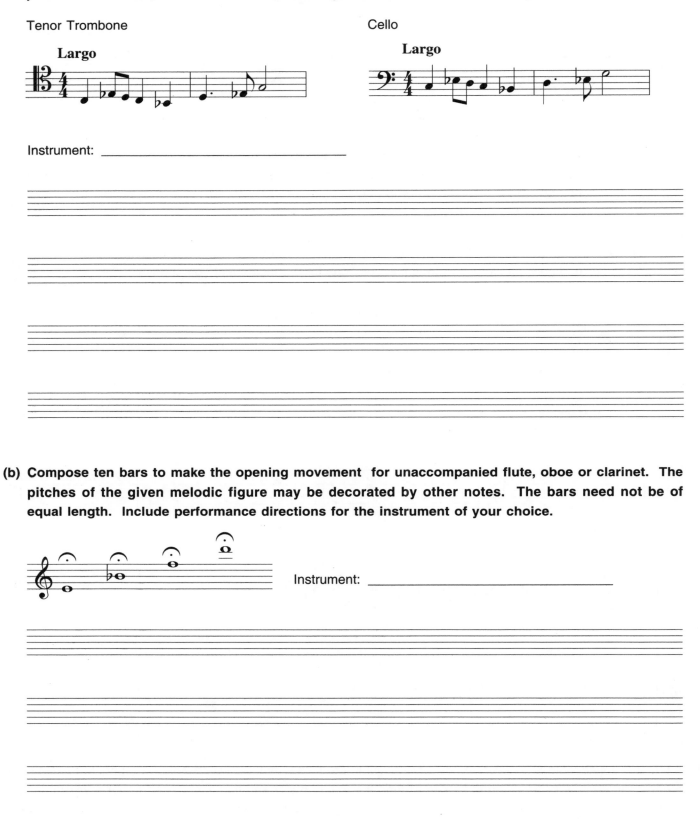

Tenor Trombone

Cello

Instrument: _____

(b) Compose ten bars to make the opening movement for unaccompanied flute, oboe or clarinet. The pitches of the given melodic figure may be decorated by other notes. The bars need not be of equal length. Include performance directions for the instrument of your choice.

Instrument: _____

(c) Compose ten bars of the opening section of a March for unaccompanied trumpet or bassoon, making use of the given opening. Include performance directions for the instrument of your choice.

Trumpet in B♭

Bassoon

Moderato

Moderato

Instrument: _____

(d) Compose about twelve bars of the beginning of a Scherzo for unaccompanied violin or flute based on the given opening. Include performance directions and bowing marks for violin.

Allegro

Instrument: _____

(e) **Compose ten bars of the beginning of a Nocturne for horn or viola, based on the given melodic line. Include performance directions for the instrument of your choice as well as bowing marks for viola.**

Horn in F

Andante

Viola

Andante

Instrument: _____

(f) **Compose about twelve bars to make the opening section of a movement for unaccompanied alto saxophone or tuba based on the given pitches. The bars need not be of equal length. Include performance directions.**

Instrument: _____

(g) Compose about ten bars of a Scherzando movement for unaccompanied flute or oboe based on the given opening. Include performance directions for the instruments of your choice.

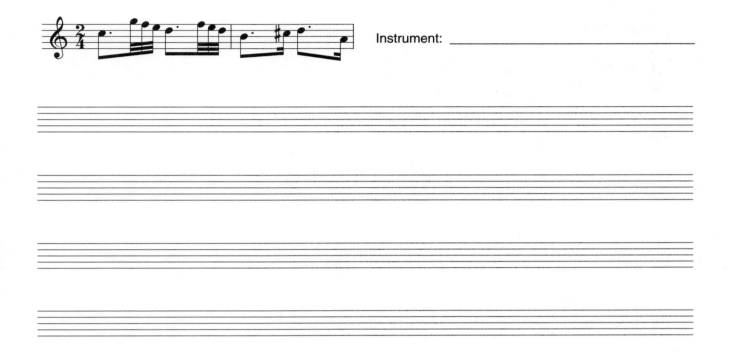

Instrument: _____

(h) Compose about twelve bars of a lyrical piece for clarinet in A or violin based on the given opening. Include performance directions for the instruments of your choice as well as bowing marks for violin.

Clarinet in A   Violin

Instrument: _____

(i) **Compose about ten bars of the beginning of a Fanfare for unaccompanied trumpet in B♭ or bassoon, making use of the given opening. Include performance directions for the instrument of your choice.**

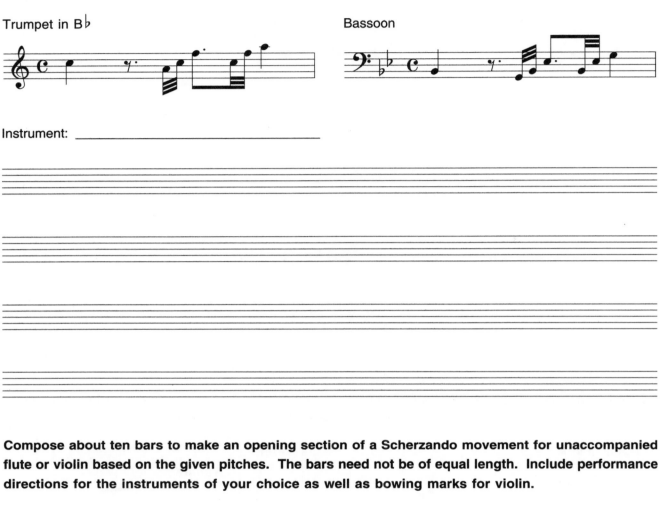

Instrument: _____

(j) **Compose about ten bars to make an opening section of a Scherzando movement for unaccompanied flute or violin based on the given pitches. The bars need not be of equal length. Include performance directions for the instruments of your choice as well as bowing marks for violin.**

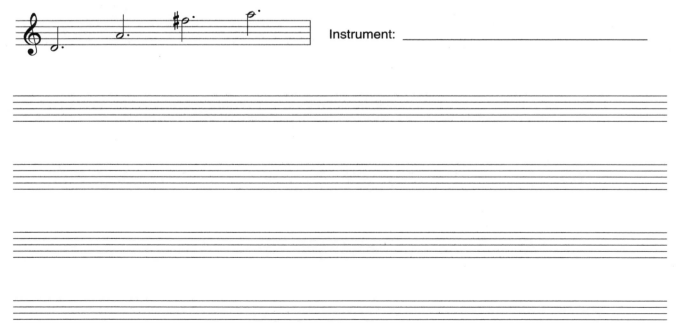

Instrument: _____

(k) Compose about ten bars of the beginning of a Tarantella (a fast dance) for unaccompanied oboe, flute or violin, making use of the given opening. Include performance directions for the instrument of your choice as well as bowing marks for violin.

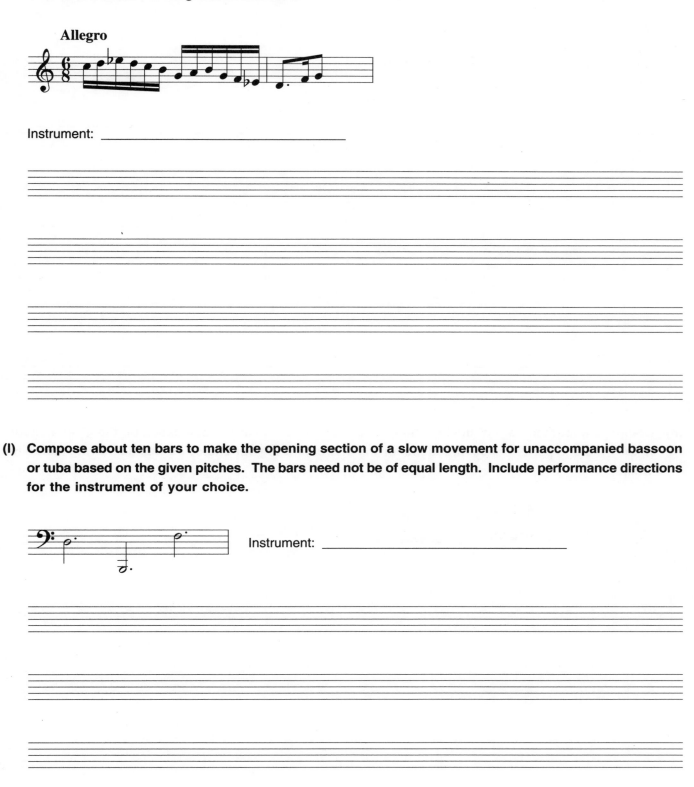

Instrument: _____

(l) Compose about ten bars to make the opening section of a slow movement for unaccompanied bassoon or tuba based on the given pitches. The bars need not be of equal length. Include performance directions for the instrument of your choice.

Instrument: _____

(m) Compose about twelve bars of the beginning of a movement for unaccompanied flute or clarinet using the given opening. The pitches of the given opening may be decorated by other notes. The bars need not be of equal length. Include performance directions for the instrument of your choice.

Instrument: _____

(n) Compose about ten bars of the beginning of a Scherzo for violin or oboe based on the given melodic figure. Include performance directions for the instrument of your choice as well as bowing marks for violin.

Instrument: _____

Things To Remember:

1) The given chords are only a harmonic framework.

2) You are not required to use all the notes of the chord.

3) Use only the notes that you think will produce an interesting melody and decorate them with melodic decorations:

   • passing notes

   • auxiliary notes (lower and upper)

   • appoggiaturas

4) Do not change the given order of the chords.

5) Use one chord for each bar unless there are more chords than the required number of bars.

6) If the number of chords are less than the required number of bars, a chord may need to be repeated.

7) End your melody with the bass note of the last chord which can be transposed into a different octave if necessary.

8) When a chord progression in a minor key ends with a major chord, the raised 3rd of the chord must be shown in the melody.

9) Keep within the range of the chosen instrument.

10) Use the correct clef for the chosen instrument.

11) Plan a time signature and rhythm that will suit the kind of melody which you are required to write.

The kinds of melodies which you are often required to write are:

• Waltz,

• Scherzo,

• Elegy,

• Nocturne,

• March,

• Ballad,

• Mazurka,

• Tarantella, etc. (see Appendix)

Example:

(a) Compose about ten bars of the beginning of a Nocturne for a flute, cello or guitar. Include performance directions and bowing marks if it is written for the cello.

Instrument: _____Cello_____

(b) Compose about ten bars of the opening section of a piece in slow waltz for unaccompanied flute, oboe or clarinet. Include performance directions.

Instrument: _____Flute_____

(a) Compose about ten bars of the beginning of an Elegy for horn or viola based on the given chord progression. Include performance directions for the instruments of your choice as well as bowing marks for viola.

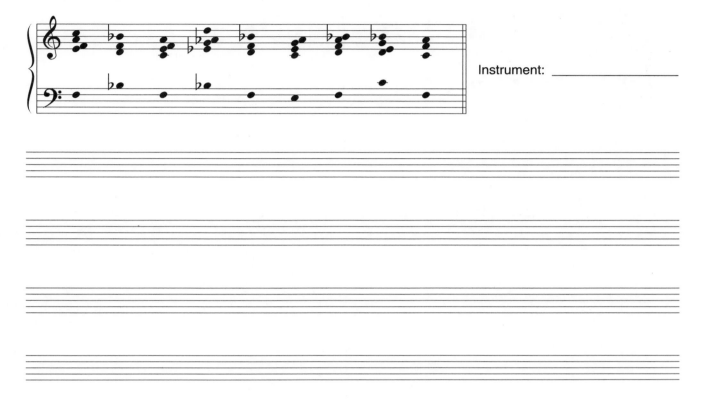

Instrument: _____

(b) Compose about ten bars of the beginning of a Mazurka for unaccompanied violin, flute or clarinet based on the given chord progression. Include performance directions for the instruments of your choice as well as bowing marks for viola.

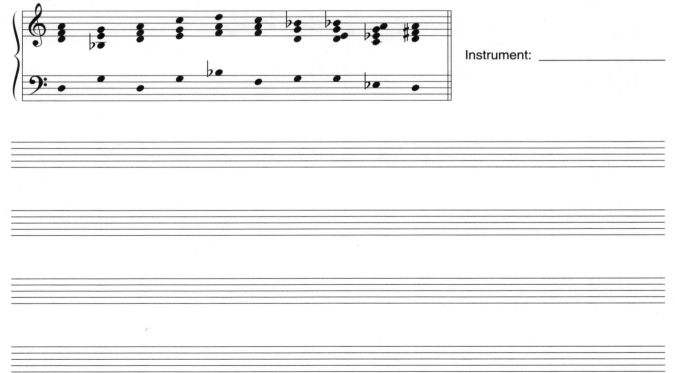

Instrument: _____

(c) Compose ten bars of a March for unaccompanied trumpet or horn based on the given chord progression. Include performance directions.

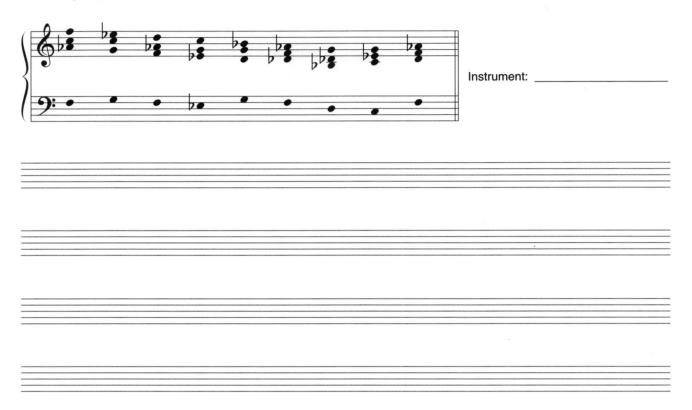

Instrument: _____

(d) Compose ten bars of a lively dance for unaccompanied violin, oboe or clarinet, based on the given chord progression. Include performance directions for the instruments you choose as well as bowing marks for violin.

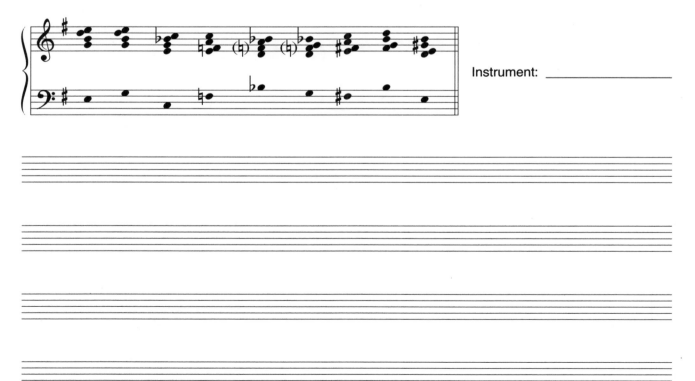

Instrument: _____

(e) Compose ten bars of a slow piece for unaccompanied cello or flute based on the given chord progression. Include performance directions for the instrument you choose as well as bowing marks for cello.

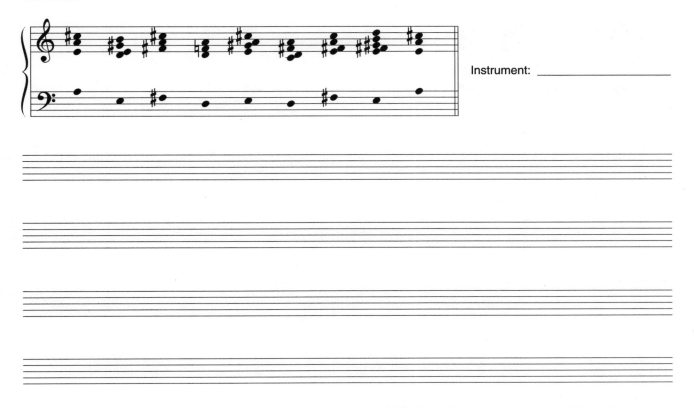

Instrument: _____

(f) Compose ten bars of a song in the style of a Ballad for unaccompanied flute, alto saxophone or viola based on the given chord progression. Include performance directions for the instrument you choose as well as bowing marks for viola.

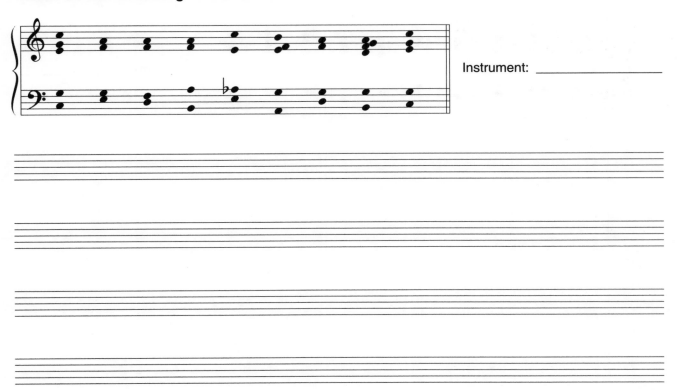

Instrument: _____

(g) Compose ten bars of the beginning of a Tarantella for unaccompanied flute or oboe based on the given chord progression. Include performance directions for the instrument you choose.

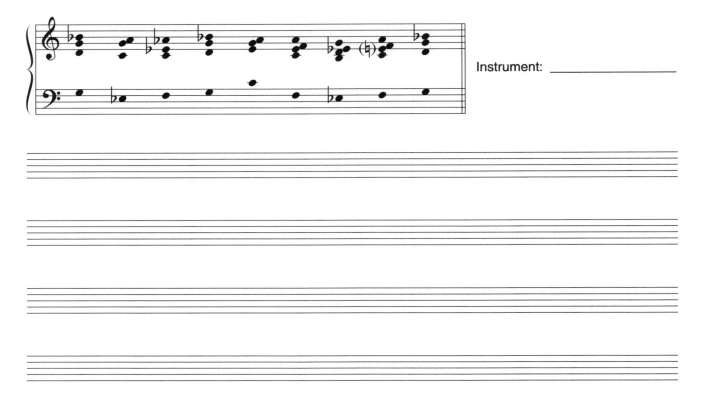

Instrument: _____

(h) Compose ten bars of a Scherzo for unaccompanied trumpet or violin based on the given chord progression. Include performance directions for the instrument of your choice as well as bowing marks for violin.

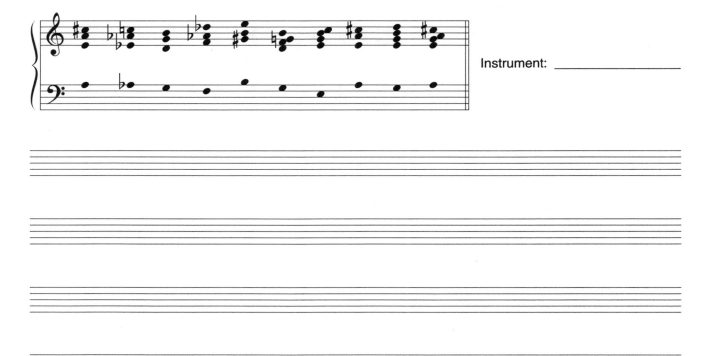

Instrument: _____

(i) Compose ten bars to make the opening section of a slow, lyrical piece for unaccompanied bassoon, cello or french horn based on the given chord progression. Include performance directions for the instrument of your choice as well as bowing marks for cello.

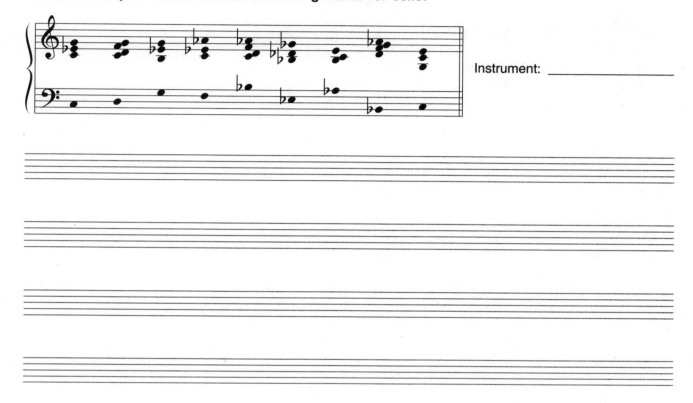

Instrument: _____

(j) Compose about ten bars of the opening of a Scherzando movement for unaccompanied oboe, clarinet or cornet based on the given chord progression. Include performance directions for the instrument of your choice.

Instrument: _____

(k) Compose about ten bars of the opening section of a slow waltz for violin or oboe, based on the given chord progression. Include performance directions and bowing marks for violin.

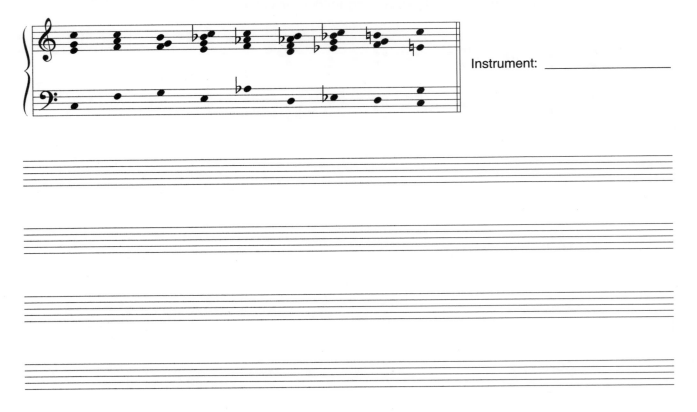

Instrument: _____

(l) Compose about ten bars of a Nocturne for unaccompanied viola, flute or guitar, based on the given chord progression. Include performance directions for the instruments you choose as well as bowing marks for viola.

Instrument: _____

BALLAD	-	A narrative song of considerable length and dramatic power.
ELEGY	-	A song of lament for the dead or for some sad events.
FANFARE	-	Flourish of trumpets or other instruments in imitation, as a means of proclamation, or a military signal.
MARCH	-	Music to accompany a group of people especially soldiers.
MAZURKA	-	A Polish national dance in triple time with an accent frequently occurring on the second or third beat of the bar.
NOCTURNE	-	A composition of a melodious and generally melancholy character which is usually played at night.
SCHERZO	-	An instrumental piece or composition of a lively and playful character.
TARANTELLA	-	A lively dance in $\frac{6}{8}$ time in which the speed tends to increase gradually.
WALTZ	-	A dance in triple time.

Just as in Grade 6, students are also required to answer questions on extracts taken from musical compositions. These musical compositions which can be from any period (Baroque, Classical, Romantic, Modern) are either solo compositions, duets, trios, quartets, quintets and full orchestras which sometimes include voices.

Students will also be asked to identify and describe chords in whatever method which has been learnt in Grade 6 - especially in the use of the Extended Roman system.

Gigue in C

1. **Study the extract printed opposite and then answer the questions below.**

a) Mark on the score, using the appropriate capital letters for identification, one example of each of the following:
   A. a 7-6 suspension in the upper part.
   B. an unaccented passing note in the bass.
   C. a supertonic seventh chord, first inversion in A minor.
   D. a perfect cadence in A minor.

b) Write out the ornament over the last note in bar 5 as it should be played.

c) What kind of chord (Augmented, Major, Minor, Diminished) is formed by the notes boxed in bar 8?

_____

d) What is a **Gigue**? _____

   _____

   i.   In what kind of work can you find Gigues? _____

   ii. At what period in the history of music can you expect to find this kind of work? _____

e) What is unusual about this Gigue as compared with the Gigues written by other composers?

   _____

   _____

   _____

   _____

2. Study the extract printed opposite and then answer the questions below.

a) i. In which key is this extract written? _____

ii. In which bar is there a modulation to B♭ major? Bar _____

b) i. Why did the composer write *p* immediately after *mf* in bars 2, 4 and 10?

_____

_____

ii. What does *sf* in bar 34 stand for and what does it mean?

_____

c) Write out the ornament in bar 17 (right hand part) as you think it should be played.

d) Mark on the score, using the appropriate letter for identification, one example of each of the following:
A. a lower auxiliary in the bass part.
B. a bar in which the treble and bass parts consist only of the notes of the dominant seventh of E♭ major.
C. an augmented 9th between the bass and treble.

e) What chord is formed by the notes boxed in the bass part in bar 16? State the key to which it belongs?

_____

f) This extract is taken from a piano sonata by Beethoven. Which of the following composers also wrote piano sonatas?

Brahms   Mendelssohn   Debussy   Chopin   Wagner

_____

Preludio

3. **Study the extract printed opposite and then answer the questions below.**

a) Give the meaning of the following:

    i.   *energico* (bar 1) _____

    ii.   *rinf.* (bar 3) _____

    iii. *sempre piu forte* (bar 8) _____

    iv. non troppo presto _____

    v. ▲ (bar 13) _____

b) Explain ➤ in bar 13 and ∧ (bar 14)_____

    Is there any different between these two signs? _____

c) Mark on the score, using the appropriate capital letter for identification, one example of each of the following:
   A. a diminished seventh chord, second inversion.
   B. a perfect cadence (Vb-I) in D minor.
   C. a dominant seventh first inversion in A minor.

d) i.   In which period in the history of music was this piece written? _____

    ii. Who do you think is the composer of this extract?
   Beethoven   Debussy   Liszt   Faure   Ravel

        _____

Le Sacre du Printemps

Stravinsky

Grade 7

4. **Study the extract printed opposite and then answer the questions below.**

a) Give the English name for each of the following instruments.

C. ing. _____

Cor. in Fa _____

Fag. _____

C. Fag. _____

b) What is the meaning of C. Fag 2 muta in Fag. 4? _____

_____

c) Comment on the parts played by Fl. picc, the second group of violin 1 and the second group of violin 2.

_____

_____

_____

_____

_____

d) Explain the sign ° above each of the notes played by the first group of violin 1.

_____

How must the violinist play these notes? _____

e) This extract is taken from Stravinsky's ballet - The Rite Of Spring. Name three composers who wrote ballets and a work by each of them.

Composer _____   Ballet _____

Composer _____   Ballet _____

Composer _____   Ballet _____

5. **Study the extract printed opposite and then answer the questions below.**

a) Give the meaning of *muta in Fl. 2.*

_____

b) Write out the part for Cor Anglais at concert pitch. Do not use a key signature but add the correct accidentals.

c) Which woodwind instrument play the same notes as the viola?

_____

d) Mark on the score, using the appropriate capital letter for identification, one example of each of the following:
A. a dominant seventh, third inversion in E♭ major.
B. Syncopation.
C. a harmonic interval of an augmented 4th.

e) This extract is taken from Walton's Concerto for Viola and Orchestra. Name one composer who wrote a Concerto for Clarinet and one who wrote a Concerto for Horn.

Concerto for Clarinet. _____

Concerto for Horn. _____

SINFONIA ANTARTICA
1. Prelude

R. Vaughan Williams

6. **Study the extract printed opposite and then answer the questions below.**

a) Give the meaning of the following:

Andante maestoso _____

dolce _____

Cantabile _____

b) Comment on the way the composer distributes the theme in the first seven bars.

_____

_____

_____

_____

_____

c) Two keyboard instruments are used in this extract - name them.

_____

d) Write out the part played by trumpet in B♭ from bars 1 to 7. Do not use any key signature but add the correct accidentals.

e) Vaughan Williams include voices in his Sinfonia Antartica (Antartic Symphony). Name two composers who also include voices in their symphonies. Give the name of the work by each of them.

Composer _____   Work _____

Composer _____   Work _____